DISNEY

CLUB
PENGUIN™

SUNBIRD

Published by Ladybird Books Ltd 2011
A Penguin Company

Penguin Books Ltd, 80 Strand,
London, WC2R 0RL, UK
Penguin Books Australia Ltd,
Camberwell, Victoria, Australia
Penguin Group (NZ), 67 Apollo Drive, Rosedale,
North Shore 0632, New Zealand
(a division of Pearson New Zealand Ltd)

www.ladybird.com

ISBN: 9781409390473
002 - 10 9 8 7 6 5 4 3 2
Printed in China

DISNEY
CLUB PENGUIN™

SHADOW GUY AND GAMMA GAL
HEROES UNITE

by Arie Kaplan
illustrated by Richard Carbajal

. . . there lived a girl called Amy! Amy was fearless.

And it was that fearlessness that led to her greatest adventure!

WHOA! IT'S . . .

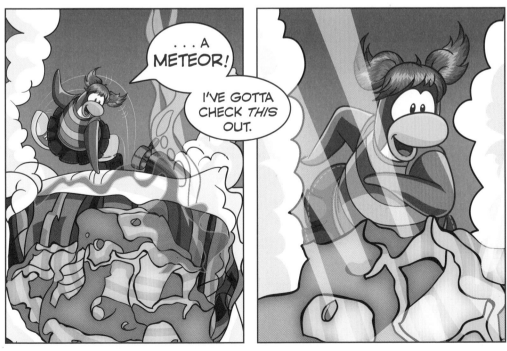

. . . A METEOR!

I'VE GOTTA CHECK *THIS* OUT.

Later, inside the Dojo . . .

SENSEI? HOW DID I GET HERE?

AH, YOU'RE AWAKE.

WELCOME TO THE DOJO, YOUNG GRASSHOPPER!

I FOUND YOU OUTSIDE, SLEEPING. YOU LOOKED SERENE, LIKE THE PEACEFUL GOLDFISH.

I HAD THE WEIRDEST DREAM, SENSEI. I DREAMED THAT THIS METEOR ZAPPED ME . . .

. . . AND SUDDENLY I WAS GLOWING!

ZAPPP!

WOW, DID YOU SEE WHAT I JUST DID, SENSEI? I ZAPPED THAT CHAIR!

GUESS IT WASN'T A DREAM.

IN YOUR HEART OF HEARTS THE METEOR IGNITED ONE GLOWING EMBER.

THE *METEOR?* IS THAT WHAT CAUSED THIS?

INDEED. THAT GLOWING ROCK MUST HAVE GIVEN YOU GAMMA POWERS.

I WONDER *WHAT ELSE* I CAN DO?

LIKE THE WISE DOLPHIN, I WILL TEACH YOU THE NINJA SKILLS NECESSARY TO HELP YOU UNDERSTAND YOUR POWERS.

OOPS. SORRY, SENSEI.

LIKE THE SLEEPY SEA OTTER, I THINK WE SHALL CALL IT A DAY.

AMY, HEED MY WORDS. NOW THAT YOU HAVE THESE POWERS, PLEASE USE THEM FOR GOOD!

AS A SUPERHERO?

YES, BUT . . .

. . . YOU NEED MORE PRACTICE. TRAIN WITH ME IN SECRECY UNTIL YOU ARE DONE.

Meanwhile, Sam, a reporter for *The Club Penguin Times*, was interviewing Gary the Gadget Guy in his lab.

WHOOPS!

THAT'S OKAY. JUST LOOK AT . . .

SORRY, I SEEM TO HAVE KNOCKED OVER SOME OF YOUR EQUIPMENT.

. . . THIS INCREDIBLE TOAST THAT THE TOASTER 3000 JUST MADE. SO CRISP, SO SWEET-SMELLING. ISN'T IT MARVELLOUS?

BUT WHAT'S THE BIG DEAL? IT'S JUST A TOASTER. A REALLY *BIG AND FUNNY-LOOKING* TOASTER, BUT STILL—IT'S *JUST* A TOASTER.

OH, YOU ARE SORELY MISTAKEN, SAM. THE TOASTER 3000 CAN DO SO MUCH MORE.

YOU CAN PLAY VIDEO GAMES ON IT.

BLIP

BLEEP

START

AND IT EVEN FEEDS YOU MILK AND COOKIES.

CHOFF
CHOFF

SNIKKT!
STTRRRK!
SPRRRK!

UH-OH!

LOOKS LIKE THE TOASTER 3000 IS EXPERIENCING AN ELECTRICAL OVERLOAD!

OH NO. IT'S GOING TO BLOW UP!

COME ON, GARY. WE'VE GOTTA GET OUT OF HERE! THIS IS DANGEROUS!

NO, SAM. I MUST STAY BEHIND AND DEACTIVATE THIS INFERNAL MACHINE.

BUT THERE'S STILL ONE THING I DON'T UNDERSTAND.

KLANG-G-LANG!

YOU WERE ZAPPED BY THE TOASTER 3000, AND YOU'RE *COMPLETELY UNHARMED.*

YEAH. IT JUST FELT . . . TINGLY.

I FEEL FINE NOW.

KAPOP!

SAM! WATCH OUT FOR THE DOOR!

WHOA! I'VE BECOME A *SHADOW.* HOW DID *THAT* HAPPEN?

THUNK!

OH MY!

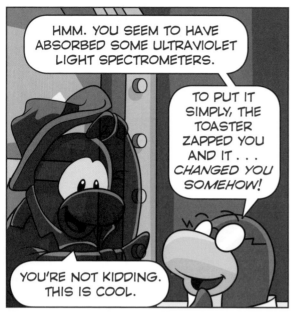

HMM. YOU SEEM TO HAVE ABSORBED SOME ULTRAVIOLET LIGHT SPECTROMETERS.

TO PUT IT SIMPLY, THE TOASTER ZAPPED YOU AND IT . . . *CHANGED YOU SOMEHOW!*

YOU'RE NOT KIDDING. THIS IS COOL.

I WONDER WHAT *ELSE* YOU CAN DO.

GUESS THERE'S ONLY ONE WAY TO FIND OUT.

LOOK! I CAN CREEP ALONG THE WALL . . .

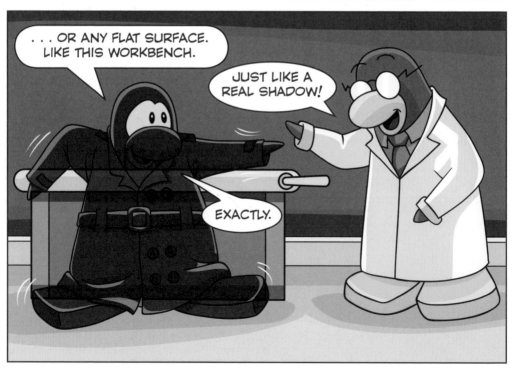

. . . OR ANY FLAT SURFACE. LIKE THIS WORKBENCH.

JUST LIKE A REAL SHADOW!

EXACTLY.

. . . AN EVEN *BIGGER* SHADOW!

I ALWAYS KNEW I WAS MEANT FOR *BIGGER* THINGS.

SAM, YOU MUST UTILIZE YOUR NEW-FOUND TALENTS FOR THE BETTERMENT OF ALL PENGUIN-KIND.

TO PUT IT SIMPLY, YOU'VE GOT TO USE YOUR ABILITIES TO HELP OTHER PENGUINS!

BUT SINCE YOU'RE STILL LEARNING TO CONTROL YOUR POWERS, YOU NEED TO TRAIN IN SECRET.

OH.

BESIDES, IT'S NOT AS THOUGH THERE'S *ANOTHER* SUPERHERO TRAINING IN SECRET HERE ON CLUB PENGUIN! WHAT ARE THE ODDS OF *THAT?*

The very next day, Sam stopped by the Pizza Parlor to grab lunch . . .

COULD I PLEASE HAVE A PIECE OF SQUID AND SEAWEED PIZZA, WITH EXTRA HOT SAUCE?

COMIN' RIGHT UP! LEMME JUST GO TO THE KITCHEN. I GOT THIS NEW PIZZA DOUGH RECIPE THAT I'M REALLY EXCITED ABOUT!

DOO-DEE-DOO! GONNA MIX UP A BATCH OF DELICIOUS *DOUGH*, DON'T YA *KNOW*, MIX IT UP, TO AND *FRO*.

DOO-DEE-DOO! GONNA MAKE A DEEP *DISH*, IT'LL BE SO *DEE-LISH*, ANCHOVY IS MY FAVOURITE *FISH*!

OH, MY CUSTOMERS WILL JUST LOVE THIS NEW PIZZA DOUGH RECIPE—

HEY, WHAT'S GOING ON? IT'S LIKE MY PIZZA DOUGH HAS COME TO LIFE!

BONK!

BONK!

BONK!

I CAN'T JUST SIT HERE WHILE THAT PIZZA DOUGH BLOB HOPS ALL OVER CLUB PENGUIN. BUT WHAT COULD I DO ABOUT IT?

HELP! MY PIZZA DOUGH HAS GONE CRAZY. SOMEONE'S GOTTA STOP IT!

AAAH!

GASP!

GULP!

HEY, WAIT A MINUTE! I'VE GOT *SHADOW POWERS* NOW! ALL RIGHT. THIS IS NO TIME TO BE AFRAID. I'VE GOT TO HELP MY FELLOW PENGUINS.

SPECIFICALLY, I'VE GOTTA GO INTO . . .

SHADOW MODE!

NOW, WHERE IS THAT PIZZA DOUGH BLOB?

THOU VILE LIVING SHADOW. WHAT ART THOU DOING?

HARK! YON SHADOW CREATURE APPEARS TO BE STEALING *OUR* SHADOWS!

TO BE OR NOT TO BE— A *SHADOW!*

SORRY, GUYS. I JUST NEED TO BORROW THESE FOR A MINUTE!

TRUST ME, FOLKS. YOU'LL THANK ME LATER.

HARRUMPH! I SHALL BELIEVE *THAT* WHEN I SEE IT.

I SEE IT. BUT I *DON'T* BELIEVE IT!

BELIEVE IT, FOLKS.

NOW IT'S TIME FOR A SNACK!

MMM! THIS IS GOOD PIZZA DOUGH.

I CAN'T BELIEVE I ATE THE WHOLE THING.

URP!

PARDON ME.

Meanwhile, on the other end of Club Penguin . . .

. . . a tree began to fall over.

When it landed, it shook up everything in the Forest, frightening all the wild puffles!

COME ON, SENSEI, WHY DON'T YOU DANCE WITH ME?

I DO NOT CARE MUCH FOR DANCING. LIKE THE GREAT GIANT CLAM, I PREFER TO REMAIN IN ONE PLACE.

LOOK, SENSEI, ISN'T *THIS* A GOOD WAY TO PRACTISE USING MY POWERS?

ER, UM . . . GLOWING LIKE A *DISCO STROBE LIGHT* IS NOT EXACTLY WHAT I HAD IN MIND. YOU SHOULD BE USING YOUR ABILITIES TO *HELP* YOUR FELLOW PENGUINS.

HELP MY FELLOW PENGUINS? HOW?

HEY! THERE ARE WILD PUFFLES EVERYWHERE! WHAT'S GOING ON??

HELP, RESCUE SQUAD! SEND SOME PENGUINS DOWN HERE IMMEDIATELY! WE'VE GOT A PROBLEM!

I REALIZE YOU RESCUE SQUAD FOLKS ARE DOING ALL YOU CAN, BUT THESE WILD PUFFLES ARE EVERYWHERE!

I KNOW, BUT WE CAN ONLY ROUND UP SOME OF THE WILD PUFFLES.

YEAH, IT'S NOT LIKE WE'RE SUPERHEROES!

IT LOOKS LIKE YOU ARE NEEDED, MY PUPIL.

THANKS, SENSEI. THIS LOOKS LIKE A JOB FOR AMY!

STORAGE CLOSET

JUST LIKE WHEN I WAS CREATING THAT *STROBE LIGHT* EFFECT, IF I *SHINE REALLY BRIGHTLY* . . .

. . . NO ONE WILL BE ABLE TO SEE WHO I AM!

HI, PUFFLES!

IT'S WORKING. THEY'RE DISTRACTED BY MY GLOW! GUESS I ALWAYS WAS A PRETTY *BRIGHT* GAL!

THAT'S RIGHT, I'M LIKE THE PIED PIPER OF PUFFLES. FOLLOW ME, MY PUFFLE PALS . . .

. . . INTO THE *PET* SHOP!

NOW ANY OF THE FOLKS ON CLUB PENGUIN CAN ADOPT THESE CUTE, LITTLE PUFFLES. THAT WAY, THEY WON'T RUN LOOSE. ISN'T THAT GREAT?

IT SURE IS! ER, BUT I HAVE A QUESTION . . .

. . . WHO ARE YOU?

WHO AM I? WELL . .

THAT'S A SECRET!

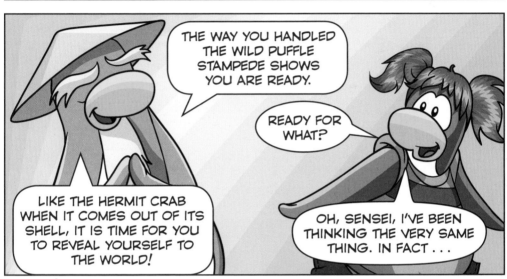

THE WAY YOU HANDLED THE WILD PUFFLE STAMPEDE SHOWS YOU ARE READY.

READY FOR WHAT?

LIKE THE HERMIT CRAB WHEN IT COMES OUT OF ITS SHELL, IT IS TIME FOR YOU TO REVEAL YOURSELF TO THE WORLD!

OH, SENSEI, I'VE BEEN THINKING THE VERY SAME THING. IN FACT . . .

THAT'S WHY I GOT THIS SUPERHERO COSTUME!

VERY IMPRESSIVE!

...GAMMA GAL!

FROM NOW ON, I'LL BE KNOWN AS . . .

Meanwhile, a similar conversation was happening over at Gary's lab.

SAM, YOU REALLY PROVED YOURSELF WITH YOUR TRIUMPH OVER THAT PIZZA DOUGH BLOB. WHICH IS WHY . . .

I SHOULD REVEAL MYSELF TO THE PUBLIC AS A SUPERHERO?

WELL, YES.

BUT WHAT WILL YOU CALL YOURSELF?

WELL, WITHOUT KNOWING IT WAS ME, AUNT ARCTIC CALLED ME "SHADOW GUY" IN THE NEWSPAPER. SO THAT'S WHAT I'LL CALL MYSELF: SHADOW GUY! NOW I JUST NEED TO FIND SOME PENGUINS WHO NEED SAVING.

THIS JUST IN! A GIANT SEA MONSTER IS STOMPING UP AND DOWN THE TOWN CENTER! THE RESCUE SQUAD AND EPF ARE OUT IN FULL FORCE, BUT IT SEEMS LIKE THIS SEA MONSTER CAN'T BE STOPPED!

TIME FOR SHADOW GUY TO SAVE THE DAY!

GOOD LUCK, SAM . . . ER, I MEAN, SHADOW GUY!

Shadow Guy zoomed toward the Town Center to stop the sea monster, not realizing Gamma Gal was up to the same thing.

THE MORE TIME I WASTE, THE MORE DAMAGE THE SEA MONSTER WILL DO. I'VE GOT TO TRY TO STOP HIM!

B-BUT, DO YOU EVEN HAVE A PLAN?

DON'T WORRY. I KNOW WHAT TO DO!

I'LL DISTRACT THE SEA MONSTER WITH SOME BRIGHT, SHINY LIGHTS.

UH, MAYBE THAT ISN'T THE BEST IDEA.

WHY NOT? IT WORKED WITH SOME WILD PUFFLES I TAMED RECENTLY.

I DON'T KNOW. THIS SEA MONSTER'S MUCH BIGGER THAN A PUFFLE.

I'M DOING IT MY WAY AND THAT'S THAT!

BUT THAT'S DANGEROUS!

WELL, I'VE MADE UP MY MIND!

WHAT ARE YOU GOING TO DO, BARGE IN THERE AND TACKLE A GIANT SEA MONSTER WITH SOME TWINKLY LIGHTS?

SEE? I KNEW YOU'D UNDERSTAND. YOU'RE THE BEST!

BUT, BUT—I DIDN'T MEAN IT LIKE THAT!

OH NO! LOOK, GAMMA GAL. YOU'VE MADE THE SEA MONSTER DIZZY!

YOU'RE RIGHT! AND NOW HE'S GOING TO . . .

. . . FALL.

CRASHHH!

GOOD THING THERE WERE NO PENGUINS INSIDE THE GIFT SHOP.

YEAH. BUT UNLESS THE SEA MONSTER IS DEFEATED, HE'LL SQUASH THIS ENTIRE ISLAND! SOMEONE NEEDS TO STOP HIM. AND THAT "SOMEONE" IS . . .

. . . ME!

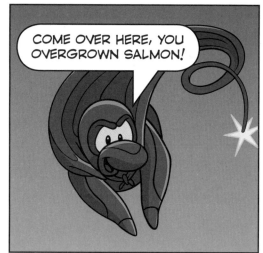

WHOOAA!

WELL, WELL, WELL . . .

SO, NEITHER OF US HAS MANAGED TO STOP THE SEA MONSTER ALONE. WHAT DO WE DO NOW?

GUESS WE BOTH STRUCK OUT, EH?

YOU KNOW, THAT MONSTER DOESN'T SEEM ANGRY OR EVEN UPSET.

GLABOOK?

HE JUST KEEPS SAYING "GLABOOK." WHAT IN THE WORLD IS "GLABOOK"?

HEY, THAT'S IT! WHY DON'T WE FIGURE OUT WHAT THIS "GLABOOK" *IS*! THEN WE CAN TAKE THE SEA MONSTER TO IT. THAT SHOULD MAKE HIM HAPPY. I DON'T THINK HE MEANS US ANY HARM.

WAIT A MINUTE, SHADOW GUY . . .

. . . YOU MEAN TO TELL ME THAT THE SEA MONSTER HAS NO IDEA THAT HE'S CAUSING ANY TROUBLE?

EXACTLY. I THINK HE'S JUST LOST, AND HE'S LOOKING FOR THIS "GLABOOK"!

NOW THAT WE KNOW THE SEA MONSTER ISN'T A BAD GUY, HOW WILL THAT HELP US STOP HIM?

HMMM . . .

I'VE GOT IT!

WOW! I'M ENORMOUS NOW. I'M ALMOST AS BIG AS THE SEA MONSTER!

HMM . . . YOU'RE STILL NOT BIG ENOUGH. NOW, GRAB THE *COFFEE SHOP'S SHADOW*, AND GRAB THE SHADOW FROM THE NIGHT CLUB . . .

. . . AND ADD *THOSE* SHADOWS TO YOU AS WELL!

WOW! NOW I'M . . .

WELL, I GUESS WE SAVED THE DAY.

YUP. AND WE DID IT *TOGETHER!*

KA-POP!

WE MAKE A GOOD TEAM!

I WONDER HOW EVERYONE ELSE IS DOING?

HELLO! I HOPE YOU DON'T MIND IF I INTERVIEW YOU FOR *THE CLUB PENGUIN TIMES*. WHAT WAS IT LIKE SAVING THE DAY FROM A FEARSOME SEA MONSTER?

UH, ACTUALLY, HE WASN'T FEARSOME.

THAT'S RIGHT. HE WAS JUST LOOKING FOR HIS FRIEND GLABOOK.

FASCINATING. SO DO YOU TWO SUPERHEROES HAVE NAMES?

YES. I'M SHADOW GUY, AND SHE'S GAMMA GAL.

BUT, SHADOW GUY, YOU FORGOT TO MENTION *THE MOST IMPORTANT PART* . . .

. . . WHICH IS THAT WE'RE A SUPERHERO *TEAM!*

WELL, GOODNESS, THAT *IS* A SCOOP! I GUESS I'LL ANNOUNCE IT TO MY READERS . . .